Pink Lady's Slipper

Jack –in –the –Pulpit

Ader's Tongue

Bloodroot

Indian Pipe

Dutchman 's Breeches

Painted Trillium

THE LEGEND OF MT. GREYLOCK;

A HISTORY OF A MOUNTAIN.

BY

Kristen H. S. Demeo

For

my father, my sons, my brothers,

and those men who have touched my life;

and inspired the story of a man and his mountain.

ISBN: 978-1-60458-683-1
Library of Congress Control Number: 2010932804

Instant Publisher
Collierville, TN 38017

2010

CONTENTS

The intent of this publication is to educate the reader about Mt. Greylock; through story, historical perspective and with ecological fact.

BOOK I: **THE LEGEND**

OF

GRAY- LOCKE

(C.1670-1750)

BOOK II: **A CONCISE HISTORY**

OF

MT. GREYLOCK

(3,491')

BOOK I:

THE LEGEND

OF

GRAY-LOCKE

(c. 1670-1750)

PRELUDE

Since I have been a young girl, the mountain has been a part of my life. Most recently, the mountain has seemed to beckon; guiding my hand, as this legend was penned.

The word legend, if one investigates, is defined as a story; handed down through the years, which contains facts; but probably is not true in itself. For example, the story of "King Arthur" is a British legend.

May you enjoy this story; that unfolds with the turning of each page.

.

THE YEAR IS 1670,

ABOUT FIVE MILES NORTHWEST OF THE

CITY OF WESTFIELD, AT THE SITE OF THE

TOWN OF WORONOCO, MASSACHUSETTS.

THERE ON THE BANKS OF THE WESTFIELD

RIVER STANDS AN ABENAKI VILLAGE OF

ONE HUNDRED WORONOKE/POCOMTUC

INDIAN.

CHAPTER I

THE SACRED MOUNT

The warm sundrenched days of summer began to fade on the banks of the Woronoco (Westfield River); and the leaves of the sturdy maples transformed their cloak from deep greens, to brilliant orange and fiery red.

A small hunting party prepared to journey west along a foot path called, the Pontoosuck. It would take many days of travel to arrive in the valley, of the Mountain. The area was heavily wooded and uninhabited by man.

The majestic mount was considered sacred and because of this, the Abenaki did not ascend its slopes. Only a foot path crossed the peak's base, on its eastern face. There the men would hunt for wild turkey, deer and pheasant.

Within days, the hunting party reached its destination. The mountain had lost its brilliant color and the upper slopes wore a deep, blue-grey hue.

Weeks passed and the hunt proved to be fruitful. One particular mourn, as the chief stepped out of his hut into the cool morning air, something was quite different. He noticed the top of the peak was frosted white. The chief thought to himself, "Winter's arrival will be soon".

When the chief left his village many weeks before; his wife was with child. He knew deep within his heart that he had become a father and it was time to return to the river valley south of the Pontoosuck.*

*

The Pontoosuck Trail was one of two foot trails that traversed Northern Berkshire. The Pontoosuck came from the south and ran along the present day West Road in Adams, MA. The other trail was the Mohawk Trail.

CHAPTER II

GRAY – LOCKE

When the party returned to the village, the chief was greeted by his wife, carrying a papoose. Lowering the tiny infant from her shoulders, she softly spoke; "Your son, my husband."

As the last warm breezes of autumn kissed the banks of the Woronoco that evening, on its shores stood a tall, proud father who cradled his infant son. A small gray tuft of hair amongst the babe's shiny black locks captured the attention of the chief. Two small bright eyes looked knowingly into his father's and a smile spread across the chieftain's chiseled jaw line.

Under a canopy of twinkling stars, the chief's weathered hands raised the child high into the night sky, toward the North Star. He proclaimed, "My son, I give you the name, Gray-Locke. Great Spirit, protect your son." "May he someday find peace in nature." With that the chief gently lowered the babe and kissed his brow, graced by the soft grey tuft of hair.

CHAPTER III

10 MOONS

Many seasons pass.

Young Gray-Locke is to turn ten moons. He knows that this will be the year that he will travel with the hunting party to the sacred mountain.

It is a warm autumn day in the valley. Indian summer has arrived. Two figures cast long shadows upon the clay earth near the river.

"Gray-Locke, my son, I give you this Abenaki Root Club*", declares the chief. Gray-Locke takes the club, holds it in his small hands and replies; "Father, what is the carving of?" "It is the head of an eagle, my son." "Aquila will guide you with his wisdom and protect you near the sacred mountain," explains the chief. "Father, I will not need the club." "Great Spirit's creatures are my friends", Gray-Locke reassures his father. "Nonsense my son, it is the wilderness", the chief replies. "I will find peace on that mountain", Gray-Locke quickly interjects.

His father looks sternly into Gray-Locke's bright eyes and says, "You must *never* climb the mountain in the west." "It is considered sacred ground to our people."* "But, father", Gray-Locke pleads. "Gray-Locke, I have spoken", commands the chief. "Go to your mother. She is waiting for you."

Gray-Locke is deeply saddened by his father's orders, but he hurries to his family's dwelling.

*

There is an actual Abenaki Root Club, with an etching of a bird's skull, on display at the Berkshire Museum, in Pittsfield, MA.

*

The Abenaki considered mountains to be sacred and because of this, they did not ascend them.

CHAPTER IV

WHEN THE LEAVES HAVE FALLEN TO SLEEP

Gray-Locke's mother is inside their wigwam. "Mother, have you ever been to the sacred mountain?" inquires Gray-Locke. "I have only journeyed there three times with your father." "It is a beautiful place of great peace," his mother replies. "What does it look like mother?"Gray-Locke asks with curiosity and wonder.

"My son, the mountain changes with the seasons." "It is as if, it were alive." "In spring, the mountain is awakened with new life." "The colors of the buds give the mountain a pink expression." As summer evolves, the mountain becomes lush, green and tranquil." "It is like a mother, with her arms outstretched, enveloping her children great and small." "Then, autumn arrives with a brilliant dance of color that decorates the mountain in celebration of harvest." "Finally, winter settles upon the mountain and it becomes almost magical, Gray-Locke; adorning itself in crystals and white."

His mother smiles with delight. "It sounds beautiful, mother," Gray-Locke says with excitement. "I will live on that mountain some day."

"Oh, no Gray-Locke, you must not go upon the mountain," his mother cautiously states. "But mother, the mountain will teach me many things that I can share with our people." "The plants and animals have stories to tell me," Gray-Locke explains.

"Gray-Locke, you have a magnificent mind, full of wonder and inquiry." "When you become chief of our people, you will do great and noble things." His mother continues, "The air near the mountain is cool and crisp and a grey lock of mist sets on her shoulders on some mornings." "Please take this black bear pelt to keep you warm at night." She gently takes her long graceful arms and wraps Gray-Locke in the fur.

Kneeling, looking into her son's bright eyes, she says; "know you are in my heart each day Gray-Locke." "You are the greatest gift I have ever received." She then kisses him gently on his pronounced little brow and smoothes the soft grey lock that falls across his forehead.

Leaving, Gray-Locke sings out; "See you when the leaves have fallen asleep mother." Gray-Locke's mother waves with assurance, yet her heart already misses him.

CHAPTER V

CLUB AND PELT

Gray-Locke runs as fast as his legs can carry him across the field. His Root Club in one hand and his bear skin in the other.

The hunting party is assembled at the edge of the village. Gray-Locke's father's bow is slung across his massive chest and a stern expression emanates from his chiseled features.

"Gray-Locke, you will soon be a man and chief of this tribe." "I expect my son to be the first brave ready, for the annual hunt." Gray-Locke looks down in shame at his little moccasins and scuffs the copper earth. He knows the trip will be long and that he must show his father how grown-up he really is.

CHAPTER VI

CRICKETS AND CATAILS

The hunting party travels many days along the Pontoosuck Trail until they come to the foot of a most massive mountain. Gray-Locke has never seen such a mountain in the valley of the river. As his tiny body stands before the mount, Gray-Locke stretches his neck upward to view the top of the peak, which seems to touch the sky.

That evening, at the base of the mountain, the hunting party makes camp next to a pond. As the sun sets in the west, the mountain slowly casts a shadow over the valley as if covering her children with a blanket. Crickets begin to chirp as cattails sway in the night breeze. *(Did you ever notice that when the sun sets, the wind always picks up a bit?)*

Gray-Locke snuggles under his bear skin and watches the flames of the fire dance and flicker in the night air. He thinks to himself, "Mother is right." "It is such a peaceful place, below this mountain." Gray-Locke closes his eyes and soon falls asleep, as birch bark* snaps and crackles on the fire, and a lone bull frog's voice echoes across the valley.

*

The Abenaki used birch bark to cover their canoes, and wigwams.

CHAPTER VII

THE HUNT

As grandfather sun climbed over the eastern ridge, mist hung heavily over the pond near camp. The cry of a jay wakes Gray-Locke. A jay always meant the season of winter was not far away. The mountain which towers before Gray-Locke is shrouded with a grey cap. "How majestic you look this morning great mountain," Gray-Locke whispers.

The camp is alive with activity, as braves prepare for the hunt. Once the hunt commences, Gray-Locke trails along behind the two parties, his Root Club slung over his small shoulder.

The day is filled with the warmth and tranquility of Indian summer.

Gray-Locke quickly looses interest in the hunt and wanders off alone. He walks for some time until he comes to a small clearing. There he lies down in the tall grass and eats black berries as he gazes up at the bright blue sky. Soon a slumbering sleep consumes the little brave.

CHAPTER VIII

THE MOUNTAIN'S MAGIC

When Gray-Locke awakes, it is afternoon. The sun is high in the sky. Sitting up, GrayLocke's eyes, heavy with sleep; adjust to the bright light. As he looks around, he notices a small trail leading into the woods before him. Something inside his soul beckons Gray-Locke forward.

As Gray-Locke enters the wooded trail, it becomes cool. The leaves rustle, as if whispering, "Welcome Gray-Locke". Rays from the bright sun, slice through the branches of the trees, creating shafts of luminous light, making the path almost magical. Walking along the trail, Gray-Locke feels peace. Fear does not exist, only wonder.

Lady fern and Golden Birch cradle the path, which is adorned with wildflowers that peek from the shadows.

As Gray-Locke treks along, he soon comes to a stream. There he rests and drinks the cool, refreshing water. The ground is now covered with a blanket of lush green fern; Gray-Locke decides to plop down. As he rolls in the bracken, his body comes in contact with a beautiful and delicate, pink flower, which resembles the moccasins he wears. Gray-Locke gently touches the flower, with the long slender neck and graceful leaves. It speaks.

"Hello young one, welcome to our mountain." "We have been waiting for you," whispers the flower. "Who are you?" inquires Gray-Locke. "I am Lady Slipper." "That is my name." "I live upon this mountain," replies the flower. "You have a soft gentle voice like my mother." Gray-Locke says as he thinks of her. "Why thank you Gray-Locke," adds the slipper.

"Hello there, son," a husky voice bellows. Gray-Locke spins around. Before him stands a dark plant with a hooded cloak. Gray-Locke thinks; how striking is he. "Jack-in-the-pulpit, at your service, I live on the mountain too." utters the straight, proud plant. "We all do," echoed many tiny voices. There in the underbrush stands a feathery green leafed shoot with ten little pairs of breeches attached to its' stem. They smile gleefully at Gray-Locke. "There are so many of you." "Are you all brothers and sisters?" asks Gray-Locke. "Yes, the white man calls us Dutchman's breeches," a chorus of voices sings.

Lady Slipper continues, "Gray-Locke, I like to introduce you to some other flowers that also live upon this mountain." "Painted Trillium, to you sir; they call me trillium because I have three leaves and three flowers upon my strong stem," he declares. "Not to interrupt but, I'm Adder's Tongue because my leaves resemble the adder," a voice quips.

All of a sudden, there is a scream. It startles Gray-Locke. "Help me," rings a tiny high pitched voice. Gray-Locke turns and runs toward the plea for help. When he reaches the plant, Gray-Locke kneels down and states, "This looks like blood." A small weak voice replies, "No, it is my root." "A fisher dug me out of the ground." "Are you bleeding?" asks Gray-Locke. "No, it is the color of my root," assuredly, the bulb replies.

Gray-Locke digs a small hole in the rich earth and places the plant in the ground and covers it. "Do you have a name," inquires Gray-Locke. "No I do not," the shoot sadly states. "Then I give you the name, Blood Root," commands Gray-Locke. "How can I ever thank you for saving my life?" The tiny plant asks. "Keep this name, I have given you," proclaims the young warrior.

Soft music begins to drift amongst the pine and beech trees. Walking towards the wafting melody, Gray-Locke pauses and says, "Its sounds like the Indian Pipe used during ceremony in our village." There near a decaying log are several white shoots that indeed resemble an Indian pipe.

"The wind blows through my petals and music is made;" replies the nodding slip. "Then you must be called, Indian Pipe;" Gray-Locke confidently announces.

As Gray-Locke searches for more wild flowers, he realizes the shadows of the trees are becoming elongated and that the sun has traveled into the western sky. "I must go!" he shouts.

Descending the trail, Gray-Locke's thighs and feet ache with each pounding step his moccasins take. Reaching the clearing, the sun has now descended over the mountain and the wind seems to echo, "*It's late*," as it nips Gray-Locke's cheeks and chin.

CHAPTER IX

PUNISHMENT

Arriving back at camp, Gray-Locke is met by his father with arms crossed and a frown of displeasure upon his face. "Gray-Locke, you disobeyed me." His voice bellows in the night air. "You left the hunting party as I asked you not to." Gray-Locke quickly interjects, "I was talking with the plants on the mountain." "They have special names father." "What!" "You climbed the mountain?" bellows his father. "Yes", Gray-Locke sheepishly replies, while looking down at his moccasins. His father lowers his voice and continues, "It is sacred ground to our people Gray-Locke." "You are the son of a chief." "As punishment for your disobedience, you will not be allowed to join the annual hunt, to this sacred mountain, for seven moons."

Gray-Locke's eyes become large, well up with tears and his lips begin to tremble with grief. As he runs back to the wigwam, his tears become blinding. Gray-Locke cannot bear the thought of not visiting his new friends.

CHAPTER X

THE WAIT

For many seasons, Gray-Locke observes the hunting party*, prepare to travel the trail without him, to the Sacred Mountain. This deeply saddens the young brave.

With the passage of seven moons, Gray-Locke becomes a tall, slender yet muscular young man, who is known for his stern gaze. He runs faster than any brave in the village and knows more about nature than anyone in the tribe. Even though he is young, he still bears a grey lock of hair which sweeps across his brow. His mother calls it, his *wisdom*. Life as a chief's son has hardened him, yet beneath his stern, rough exterior; a kind, gentle soul still resides.

*

In the Abenaki culture, each man had a different hunting territory, inherited from his father.

CHAPTER XI

THE WORLD NOT SO BIG

The year has come for Gray-Locke to travel again, to his magical mountain. When the day finally arrives, Gray-Locke is filled with excitement and joy. He is the first brave ready for departure. As the party is preparing to embark, his father approaches him and says, "Gray-Locke, you make me proud that you *are*, the chief's son." This makes Gray-Locke feel as if he has finally earned his father's forgiveness for so many moons ago.

The trail seems shorter this time and the world not so big. As the party enters the valley of the sacred mountain, Gray-Locke is over come with a great sense of peace. The mount has only autumn's color half way up its slopes and the summit displays a blue-grey hue.

When the next morning arrives, Gray-Locke wakes with the first light. Two hunting parties prepare to set out once again along the foot path used for so many generations. Gray-Locke secretly plans to venture off to the south, to find the trail in the clearing, amongst the sturdy maples.

CHAPTER XII

THE SUMMIT

With persistence and instinct, Gray-Locke comes to where he rested as a boy. Memories rush back of eating black berries and lying in the tall grass, as the warmth of autumn caressed his young face. There before him lies the trail that beckoned his spirit onward years before. His goal: to reach the summit.

Traveling the path, Gray-Locke begins to recognize that this is in fact his trail. The trunks of the maple and beech, which line the path reveal his etched symbols of long ago. The markings are a bit higher, yet Gray-Locke still has to scan the trunks carefully to identify each mark.

As he climbs, he begins to notice the tree line also becomes shorter. Balsam Fir now dominates the landscape. In one particular place on the mountain, it looks quite unusual. The area consists of three slopes that surround a small valley; where many, many Red Spruce stand tall. Gray-Locke pauses to admire the beauty of this place. It is as if Great Spirit has made a special clearing in the forest so one can view this piece of nature's art. For a moment in time, the little boy with the wonderful imagination returns. Gray-Locke thinks to himself, "If I were a giant, I could hop from one slope to the next." "I'd be a hopper." "I call this place, the *Hopper*." Gray-Locke is suddenly startled from his inner dialogue by a loud snapping of branches in the thicket nearby. As he stands as still as a pond's surface and waits; a large black bear appears and then traverses the slope on its venture down the mountain.

Gray-Locke encounters an abundance of wildlife on this day. A porcupine waddles along the path he travels. A white tail deer grazes in a clearing filled with golden rod, and a bobcat navigates a stony ledge. He also discovers a small triangular cave that glitters with gold, as a raven perches on a rock nearby. Gray-Locke names this spot, "Raven's Rock"*, for he and the raven only know his discovery.

Gray-Locke never reaches the summit on this particular day. He knows he must return to camp and contribute to the hunt. He begins his descent down the mountain. Thundering down the trail, as he had done as a young boy, pheasant and turkey are flushed out of the underbrush.

CHAPTER XIII

FIRE-LIGHT

Upon entering camp, Gray-Locke carries two large turkeys and an amber colored pheasant over his lean shoulders. Pheasant will be his dinner, this clear star lit night.

That evening, Gray-Locke keeps to himself and watches the fire embers spark and crackle. He thinks about his day upon mountain, with all its beauty and peace.

He makes a promise to himself, to travel alone to his sacred mountain, when he becomes eighteen moons. His thoughts are interrupted by his father's deep voice. "Gray-Locke, you went out on your own today?" his father inquires. "Yes father, I prefer to hunt alone." Gray-Locke replies as he stares at the flames. "Someday you will lead our people." "Others will look to follow you. Gray-Locke." remarks the chief. Gray-Locke refutes, "Father in order to lead we must know ourselves." "On the mountain..." "What Gray-Locke?" questions his father. "I meant that hunting alone beneath the sacred peak helps me to prepare to lead." "I am tired father and morning light will come soon." the brave replies with pause. "You have spoken with much wisdom, my son, good night." Gray-Locke utters automatically, "Good night to you father." Yet his thoughts are atop the mountain.

*

Raven's Rock is an actual mountain cliff located near Mt. Greylock. It has an elevation of 1581'.

CHAPTER XIV

HIS MANITOU

Another year passes and the valley prepares for winter once again. The air is colder and the trumpeting geese have flown south, a month past. Gray-Locke is now eighteen moons and considered a man, a warrior and hunter in the Abenaki tribe.

To prove he has become worthy of this passage; Gray-Locke goes to his parents and states, "Father and mother, I have decided to travel to the sacred mountain as proof that I may take my place as a man, hunter and some day chieftain of our tribe." "I will be gone until the wide river is frozen in our valley."

"It is so far to travel alone, Gray-Locke", says his mother, softly. "The distance will strengthen me", replies Gray-Locke. "My son, winter will have settled in near the sacred mountain", his father states with concern. "It will sharpen my survival instincts", Gray-Locke assures them. "This is what I have chosen as my challenge." His eyes search his parent's for acceptance. Gray-Locke's mother instinctively embraces her son and the chief nods with approval.

The cry of a jay wakes Gray-Locke at dawn. Excitement rumbles in his belly. The day has finally come to journey along the Pontoosuck to the valley of the mountain. Gray-Locke sets out with his bow and arrow, a large bear skin and a small provision of dried venison.

When Gray-Locke arrives at the base of the sacred mountain, several inches of snow covers the ground, where the hunting party usually pitches camp. The top of the peak is frosted white. Gray-Locke decides to spend the night at the base and set out at dawn, to ascend to the summit.

The forest is still as if it were asleep for the winter. Not a plant can be seen nor song of a bird heard; except for an occasional jay, who shouts that the mountain has a visitor. The climb is slow and exhausting, but Gray-Locke does not turn back. He knows it will develop his perseverance. "You mustn't give up", his mind shouts. "I will, reach the top", is the chant that propels him forward. Gray-Locke stops only once, to drink cold water from a mountain stream and eat a bit of pemmican. As he rests, he notices the tree line. Many Balsam Firs now dot the steep slopes of the mountain and the peak is in sight. As Gray-Locke climbs the last part of the ascent, the bows of the trees hang heavy with white snow. Gray-Locke thinks to himself, "This is truly a magical world only known to Great Spirit." "Mother's description of this wintry place, so many moons ago, is everything she described."

Reaching the summit, Gray-Locke walks to a ledge that overlooks the valley below. It is where the hunting parties pitched camp for generations; near the pond and willows.

The view is unbelievable. It is as if Gray-Locke is standing near the throne of Great Spirit, looking over his entire domain. The moment fills Gray-Locke with deep peace and an awakening. Words just seem to flow from his lips; "Great Spirit, I promise to preserve and protect this mountain and all of nature that resides upon its slopes." "May this mountain bear the name, Mt. Gray-Locke; the sacred ground, forever."

A tear cascades down Gray-Locke's chiseled face. The young Indian of Pocumtoc descent stands alone on the wintry summit. A black bear pelt drapes over his broad shoulders, a single eagle feather is his head dress and weathered deerskin leggings, soaked with new fallen snow, cover his legs that are as solid as the trunk of any maple.

As the morning sun begins to climb slowly into the eastern sky, Gray-Locke's attention is quickly captured by random tuffs of smoke billowing up from the valley below. He knows this to be the fire of the white man, and what it means for his people and possibly his mountain. A deep sadness washes over Gray-Locke's face as he looks northward at the range which goes on forever.

Gray-Locke decides to spend the night atop the mountain. The wind hollows as snow spins and swirls across the moon lit summit. Even though Gray-Locke is alone, he feels safe and content in nature.

When morning comes, Gray-Locke's bear pelt is covered with a fresh blanket of snow. The fur has turned white. As Gray-Locke stands and shakes the fur, the shiny black coat reappears. It startles a snow shoe rabbit, who quickly hops out of sight. A slender grey fox braves the bitter cold, morning air, to hunt for breakfast, as Gray-Locke readies for his descent down the mountain.

The trek home seems to take Gray-Locke less time, after trudging through the mountain snows. When his finally reaches his village, he is happy to see his parents, yet his heart longs for his mountain. It is also a place he now calls his "home".

CHAPTER XV

A GENTLE HEART BROKEN

Many seasons come and go, and with the seasons come war and disease. Gray-Locke's father is killed during battle, in the Three Years War. His mother soon follows, taken by the epidemic that sweeps through the valley, two summers past.

Gray-Locke is thrust into the position of chieftain, leader of his people. His gentle heart hardens and his thoughts are dominated by anger and resentment. For he believes it was the white man's rifle and disease that took the two people he loved most, from his life. His light-hearted smile turns into a frown and soon he becomes known as the "frowning chief of the Woronokes."

Life becomes even harder for him to bear. In the years that follow, the Abenaki and settlers battle for the land around the sacred mountain. By 1727, the Abenaki people concede the sacred mountain to the Massachusetts settlers in order to make peace and soon tribes travel northward into Canada.

Chief Gray-Locke becomes a prominent chief amongst his people and is considered, their greatest leader.

Gray-Locke makes repeated efforts to curb the state of affairs, for he knows in his heart that the white man will only take from nature and not restore its balance. As a result, the chief is often heard stating; "this land we live upon, does not belong to any man; red, white or brown; we only borrow it for a time, while we are on this journey upon mother earth."

When all peaceable attempts fail at saving the sacred mountain, Gray-Locke leaves his daughter and son, the charge of leading his people northward into Canada. Even though the family pleads with their father to join them, Gray-Locke refuses. He takes a small band of warriors westward to live a top Mt. Gray-Locke. There he begins to conduct guerilla raids on the settlers of Western Massachusetts and Southern Vermont. He continually eludes his pursuers and acquires the name amongst his people as *"wawanolet"*, which means "he who fools and puts others off track." Even though Gray-Locke* becomes driven by his quest; many a night and at early dawn he stands on the summit and looks mournfully northward, wondering the fate of his people, his wife and his children.

As far north as Canada, his war becomes known as "Gray-Locke's War", because it is fought for his own reasons and not for the agenda of the white man.

*

Records do in fact reveal there was a Native American Chief, Gray-Locke, who lived from 1650-1750, and was born near Westfield, Massachusetts. In the 1700's this was the correct spelling of his name.

CHAPTER XVI

THE FINAL PEACE

For more than twenty years, Gray-Locke lives on the mountain. His small band of warriors is either killed in raids or by sickness. Those who are left eventually retreat north.

Gray-Locke becomes an aged old chief who walks with a limp and totes a staff that resembles his Abenaki Root Club, from his youth. He is now alone. His home becomes caves that he uses for shelter. Some of the caves contain gold and Gray-Locke resorts to trading the gold as well as animal pelts, with settlers for supplies he needs to survive.

He becomes known as the "Old Indian" or the "Man of the Mountain"; with the high brow, gray locks and an eternal frown. Living on the mountain does indeed have a transforming effect on the old chief. With the passage of time, Gray-Locke once again begins to find his peace in nature and his heart softens.

The last known account of the chief is in the year, 1750. The winter snows last on the mountain and in the valley until the month of May. Many people and wild life die due to the shortage of food.

In the late spring of 1751, a trapper comes off the mountain to trade pelts with the settlers. He carries with him a staff he finds on the summit. The top of the single-stick bares the carving of an eagle's head, resembling the root clubs of the Abenaki who once resided in the river valley to the east. The most magnificent claim made is that symbols found on the staff, spell the Abenaki word, "wawanolet", which is also synonymous with the meaning, "sacred ground."

For years stories continue to travel about the old Indian. Some say they spot him on the eastern face of Greylock's summit, looking longingly northward. Others say he still lives in the caves, changing his gold into "fools' gold", for settlers, who chance to prospect.

Chief Gray-Locke would have lived to be eighty years of age; a very rich and long life during a period of time, when the life expectancy of a Massachusetts's settler was only thirty- thirty five years.

CHAPTER XVII

FACT

These stories eventually faded too, as do the colors of an autumn landscape.

The industrial revolution nudged at the door of a new century and the iron horse soon changed the valley's scenery forever.

In the years that followed, immigrants who settled the valley did deforest the eastern slopes of the mountain in the late 1800's.

Over the years, many have found gold's cousin, *fool's gold* in the caves on its eastern face. A trail does ascend the mountain from the south east. It is called the Cheshire Harbor Trail and the site of the annual Greylock Ramble, which occurs each year on Columbus Day Weekend.

If you have a chance to partake in traveling this trail, may you also find nature's peace.

REFLECTION

Why did this land slide occur in May of 1990?

Was it a random act of nature or nature's art?

If nature's art; is it a pictorial depiction, of a history of a life, that holds a message for those who dwell upon this earth today?

Over the years that I have observed this landslide, the image has seemed to transition through a life cycle.

When the slide first occurred, it resembled a man's profile. At closer inspection, the image of a Native American was clearly discernable. A pronounced brow, chiseled features and a solemn expression became its signature.

This image also has expressed youthfulness, anger and even hope. As years have passed, the face has begun to reflect a more tired, aged, almost mournful man, who faces north.

Sadly, the image has begun to fade. In only one season does nature touch the canvas of this stone. The season is winter. Nature dusts the stone with a light covering of snow. This seems to create life within the sculpture; so much so, to even fashion the ocular bone and lid of an Indian's profile, as depicted on the cover of this book.

As I was completing the last pages of this creation, spring was welcomed into our valley. Gazing up at the image, I noticed to its left, for the first time, another image. It resembles a bird, could it be Aquila?

If you happen to travel to Berkshire County, and pass through the town of Adams, remember to look westward.

AUTHOR'S NOTE

My sense, after all the research I have done and the number of hours I have contemplated the image upon the mountain, I derived this message;

"Stand for that which you believe in."

"Be determined about your convictions."

May this ancient mountain hold a message for you,

Be Well.

BOOK II:

A
CONCISE
HISTORY
OF
MT. GREYLOCK
(3491')

A History of A Mountain

Welcome to the highest peak in the state of Massachusetts, Mt. Greylock (3491'). It lies 130 miles from the Atlantic Ocean and is a member of the oldest mountain chain within the Americas.

The Beginning

Some 500-600 million years ago, during a time of intense mountain building, Greylock and the accompanying range came into existence, as the result of a process known a Thrust Faulting. This is a phenomenon in which older rock is thrust up above younger rock. In the case of Mt. Greylock, schist and quartzite rose above younger limestone and marble.

The schist that exists on Mt. Greylock is called Greylock Schist. It has a grayish pigmentation and can be found in abundance on the reservation. This erosion resistant stone makes up the back bone of the mountain. Quartz can also be found on the reservation and is identified as a milky, white stone usually embedded in the schist. The Native Americans who frequented the area used the quartzite to make arrow heads and other tools.

If opportunity arises to explore the trails or travel the road system to the summit, Greylock Schist can be readily identified and seen along the road ways close to the summit.

After this period of intense mountain building ended, Greylock rose some 20,000 feet and was surrounded by an ancient sea with a maximum depth of 500 feet. For millions of years that followed, an abundance of shellfish and silt deposited at the bottom of this sea, which contained coral reefs similar to those in the South Pacific.

As a result of these deposits, the "Berkshire Buffer" was created. It is a large concentration of limestone that lies in the valley below Mt. Greylock. It has been mined for its use, to the present day for pharmaceuticals, fertilizers and much more. Presently, mining of this limestone is occurring fifty feet below Route 8 which passes to the east of the deposit, in the town of Adams. The facility, Specialty Minerals, offers tours of the 150 year old limestone quarry and mining site. This limestone "buffer" also protects the area from the worst effects of acid rain.

Close to 200 million years, the climate began to change and temperatures dropped. As a result, the ice age commenced, covering Mt. Greylock and the surrounding region in sheets of ice up to a mile (1km), in thickness.

Time passed, and at 100,000 years, glaciers arrived in the Berkshires. These giants carved the north-south, U-shaped valleys of Berkshire County and rounded off Mt. Greylock and the surrounding ranges. The process is known as Glaciation.

The Mountain's Ecosystem

The mountain consists of three zones.

The first zone is considered the lower slopes. The area is predominantly Northern Hardwoods. This means the trees are typically straight and tall; such as the Sugar Maple, Beech, or Poplar.

At approximately 2,300 feet, the second zone begins. It is called the Transitional Forest. It is an area where taller vegetation transitions to shorter. The area can have tall Spruce, Maple and Birch as well as shorter Balsam fir or Mountain Ash.

This area also contains the most southern glacial feature of New England, "The Hopper". It is an area of land where a semi-circular valley is surrounded on three sides by steep slopes. Designated as a National Natural Landmark, this region contains tree species up to350 years old and boasts a Red Spruce, 120 feet (37)km tall. Traveling Rockwell Road to Greylock's summit, one can view the Hopper from the New Ashford Overlook and across the valley, the site known as Stony Ledge.

Locals consider Stony Ledge to be one of the most scenic vistas to view the landscape of this mountain range. A two mile hike (round trip), along Sperry Road would bring one to this destination. Information about such trails can be obtained at the Greylock Visitors Center in Lanesborough on Rockwell Road.

The third and final zone is located on the summit of Mt. Greylock. A distinct boundary exists between hardwoods and the boreal forest at this elevation, beginning at approximately 2600 feet. It is the only place in Massachusetts where this taiga/boreal forest exists and the southernmost occurrence of this type of forest in North America.

The terrain of the mountain is dominated by the Balsam Fir, because of its' resistance to cold temperatures. This particular tree also possesses pliable limbs can that hold the weight of snow and ice that accumulates on the peak. Cloud cover tends to hang longer at this elevation too; drenching vegetation with an abundance of moisture.

The area is also known for its *Flag Trees*. It is a phenomenon where prevailing winds over time damage as well as kill the exposed side of a tree. As a result, a tree's growth begins to resemble a flag blowing in the wind. Trees of this orientation can be seen on the summit as well as near the Adams Overlook, which is a spectacular vista for moonlit star gazing or for a panoramic viewing of the Berkshire Valley below.

Flora

The mountain is home to many wild flowers, such as; the Trillium, Blood Root, Dutchman's Breeches, Lady Slipper, Jack-in-the Pulpit, Queen-Anne's Lace, Indian Pipe, Black –Eyed Susan, Fern, Bluets, Partridge Berry, and Mt. Blueberry; to name a few.

Photographs of many of these wildflowers are on display at the Visitor Center on Rockwell Road. Natural flora can also be discovered on the summit and along the trails which ascend Mt. Greylock's slopes.

Wild Life

Some of the animals and birds that inhabit the mountain include; the Gray Squirrel, Chipmunk, Pheasant, Wild Turkey, Bobcat, White-Tailed Deer, Black Bear, Fisher, Raccoon, the Warbler, Sparrow, Robin, Blue Jay, Grosbeak, Wood Pecker, Rabbit, Porcupine and the Great Horned Owl.

Many of these mammals and birds can also be viewed at the Visitor Center, where they are displayed.

The origin of the Mountain's name

The origin of the mountain's name is still unclear. It first appeared in print in 1819. There are two theories. The first is that the summit of Mt. Greylock often has a grey cloud or lock of grey mist that sets on its peak and so the name was derived from this attribute. The second postulate is that the mountain was named in tribute to a legendary Native American chief, Gray Locke, who was born near Westfield Massachusetts in 1670. For a period of time before this name was given to the mountain, the mountain was called the Grand Hoosuck.

The Reservation

On July. 20, 1885, 400 acres were purchased by the Greylock Park Association, in order to preserve the mountain and its surrounding land. By 1898, Massachusetts created the first state park, the Mt. Greylock Reservation. Today, the reservation boosts an area that covers 12, 500 acres and includes 70 miles of trails.

During the Great Depression, President Roosevelt created the Civil Conservation Corps, (CCC). It was an organization that brought jobless men to parklands across the nation, to create public recreational facilities. The 107th Company worked and lived on Greylock, between 1933-39. This corp of men developed the road systems, completed the Bascom Lodge and created the Thunderbolt Ski Run, as well as constructed many shelters, trails and scenic vistas.

The Bascom Lodge

The lodge was built between 1933-38, using native materials, consisting of Greylock schist, Red Spruce and Oak. The structure was designed by Pittsfield Architect, James McArthur Vance. Once the lodge was built it was named in honor of John Bascom.

John Bascom, (1827-1911) was a professor at Williams College and later served as one of the first commissioners of the Greylock Reservation. In 1907 Bascom wrote a twenty page pamphlet, touting the need for lodging on the summit. Bascom wrote, "The most urgent need is a fitting reception house on the summit." "The object should not be to civilize the mountain, but to bring over civilized men of the valley into complete contact with it. … simply to preserve the fine handiwork of nature." Unfortunately, Bascom did not live to see his vision become a reality.

Most recently, the lodge has been beautifully renovated and offers lunch, dinner and overnight accommodations for any a weary traveler. John Bascom would be pleased. One can contact the Bascom Lodge at (413)-743-1591.

The Tower

The 92 foot granite War Memorial Tower stands atop of Mt. Greylock and affords a 360° view of five states. The translucent globe is illuminated by six lights and is said to be visible for 70 miles. At one time, it was the strongest beacon in Massachusetts.

Originally the tower was to serve as a light house on the Charles River in Boston. Then in 1930, with the support of Senator Plunkett of Adams, plans changed for this pillar and it was to be built atop Mt. Greylock. In 1933, the tower was dedicated as a war memorial to honor Massachusetts men and women who gave their lives in time of war.

Residents of the area advocated the use of local stone in the construction of the monument, but ultimately quarried granite from Quincy, Massachusetts was delivered, to create the 28 meter shaft.

Ironically, a tower that was intended to be a light house now sits atop a mountain that was once surrounded by ancient sea.

The Visitor Center

The Greylock Visitor Center is located on Rockwell Road in Lanesborough Massachusetts. It is open year round and provides travel and trail maps, informational brochures, exhibits and accessible rest rooms. The center can be contacted by phone at (413)-499-4262 and is open year round, seven days a week.

DID YOU KNOW?

1. Mt.Greylock was inspiration for many writers.

Herman Melville, in 1850-51, set up an observation deck at his Arrowhead home in Pittsfield Massachusetts, to gaze upon the mountain. It is said that the grey mist atop Greylock's peak was inspiration for the white whale in *Moby Dick*. Melville also dedicated his next novel, "Pierre", to Mt. Greylock.

Henry David Thoreau, in July of 1844, ascended Mt. Greylock and wrote of his experience. This excursion served as a prelude for his rugged individualism at Walden Pond in 1845.

Nathaniel Hawthorne also climbed Mt. Greylock several times. These experiences influenced his work, "The Unpardonable Sin."

The country's first native born poet, *William Cullen Bryant* was also inspired to write poetry about the peak and streams of this majestic mountain.

2. The northeastern slopes of Mt. Greylock became a stop for the Underground Railroad during the mid 1800's. A number of runaway slaves lived in log cabins on the mountain in quest for freedom. It has been said that John Brown himself may have been hosted in the Cheshire Harbor.

3. Mt. Greylock is the highest peak in Southern New England.

4. The Appalachian Trail passes over Greylock's summit on its way from Georgia to Maine.

5. *Abenaki*- pronounced (AH-buh-nah-kee) belonged to the Algonquian people of North Eastern North America, and were known as the; "the people" or "easterners."

The Abenaki were also known as the keepers of stories. Story telling was very important to their culture. Both genders took part in this ritual. Stories were also means of teaching children behavior. The Abenaki believed children were not to be mistreated, instead of punishing, a child would be told a story.

The Western Abenaki lived mostly in the Connecticut River Valley. They existed as small bands of extended families. In spring and summer, these bands came together near rivers such the

Westfield and Connecticut. These villages usually numbered about 100 people. The men were the hunters and fishermen. Each man had a hunting territory inherited through his father. The women were the care givers and farmers. They planted the "sisters", a stalk of corn, supporting beans and squash. The women also harvested berries and made maple syrup. Children were also expected to contribute to the tribes' existence. They went hunting and fishing with their fathers and had more chores and less time to play, than children of today.

The Abenaki lived in dome shaped, birch bark dwellings; yet some had teepees resembling those of the Great Plains. The chief was always a man and the headdress he wore was usually a single eagle feather. Today, a woman can be a chief too. The women wore their hair loose or braided on top of their heads. The men also wore their hair long and loose until they had a girl friend or were married, then it was tied back.

The use of the birch bark canoe and dog as a pack animal, dominated the Abenakis' mode of transportation. In winter months, wigwams were lined with bear and deer skin for warmth.

Their form of government was based on group decision making, done by consensus. It was based on the idea that every family, band or tribe had equal say. The goal was for total understanding of all members. Decisions were arrived at by considering three truths: peace; (Is it preserved?), righteousness; (Is it moral?) and power; (Does it preserve the integrity of the group?).

6. Three trails ascend the eastern face of Mt. Greylock. The *Cheshire Harbor Trail*, the most gradual, is less than a two mile hike and is where the Greylock Ramble commences each year in October. The second is the *Gould Trail* which is the most direct and strenuous. It ascends 2100 feet and covers 3.2 miles of terrain. It is named after a family farm where the trail originates. The third is the *Thunderbolt Trail*. Created by the CCC as a world class downhill race course, in the 1940's; this strenuous trail takes approximately two hours or more to ascend. The is trail, named after a roller coaster ride at Revere beach in Massachusetts, gives one an idea of the terrain.

Most recently, a new generation of back country skiing enthusiasts; the Thunderbolt Ski Runners refurbished the entire trail. Locals say it is in the best shape since the 1950's. In the winter of 2010, the *Runners* held the first Thunderbolt Race to be run in 75 years. To learn more about the club or the history of the *Thunderbolt* refer to the source page in the back of this publication.

7. A *statue* stands in Battery Park in Burlington, Vermont in honor of the Abenaki's greatest leader, Chief Gray Locke. The Totem is carved out of a single red oak tree and is mounted on red sand stone.

8. The *weather* recorded for the year of 1750 revealed that it was extremely cold and snow lasted at higher elevations until the month of May. As a result, many animals and people died, due to the shortage of food and prolonged cold temperatures.

9. The 1500 foot landslide to the left of the image of the Native American on Greylock's eastern face occurred in 1901 and is referred to as "the chief's steps".

10. In May of 1990, after four days and four nights of rain, a large land slide occurred on the eastern face of Mt. Greylock. As a result of the slide, a giant stone profile was left in its wake, which seemed to watch over the land.

Glossary

Aquila- an eagle.

Bracken- large fern.

Fisher- a carnivorous mammal of the weasel family and inhabitant of North America.

Fool's Gold- is Iron Pyrite. It resembles gold in appearance, yet when nitric acid is applied to the crushed stone, the pyrite is dissolved by the acid. Gold would not disintegrate if nitric acid is applied.

Hopper- one who hops; or a funneled shaped chamber that gathers grain for farmers.

Iron Horse- the name given to the steam engine that rode the rails across America.

Manitou- is an Algonquian religious belief, in a spirit or god. Every boy had to receive a message in order to take his place as a man and hunter in his tribe. The brave would know how to recognize the message. It may come in the form of a dream, experience or through an animal.

Papoose- a young child of American Indian parents.

Pemmican- is deer meat that is mixed with crushed choke cherries or berries, and then dried.

Root Club- a club made from a root of a tree.

Venison- another word for deer meat.

Sources Cited:

Clermont, Paul. "Time Pieces: Life in the Berkshires and Beyond", *Greylock for Breakfast*, 219-20. (Notch Publishing, 2007).

Michalenko, Eugene F. "In this Valley: A concise History of Adams, Massachusetts." (Adams Speciality and Printing Company, Adams Massachusetts, September 2000, revised July 2002), 5-6.

Mark Rondeau, "The Greylock Reservation Project: Discovering my own Backyard" II. Natural History and Topography", http://markrondeau.com/greylocktwo.html (accessed 3/10/2010).

Mark Rondeau, "John Bascom and Mount Greylock" http://markrondeau.com/johbascom.html (accessed 3/10/2010).

Thunder Ski Runners "Thunderbolt" www.thunderboltskirunners.org (accessed 10/25/09).

Wikipedia, "Abenaki", http://en.wikipedia.org/wiki/Abenaki (accessed 7/30/2009).

Wikipedia, "Mount Greylock", http://en.wikipedia.org/wiki/mount greylock (accessed 5/27/2009).

"Mount Greylock's Hidden Treasures: A Driving Tour", www.mass.gov/massparks, printed 2004.

Herbert S. Zim, Ph.D and Alexander C. Martin, Ph.D. *Flowers: A Guide to American Wildflowers*. Golden Press. New York, 1987.

Sources continued:

The Golden Home and High School Encyclopedia., "Massachusetts", 1572-1573, Vol.11 (Golden Press:New York, 1961).

Michael Bobowiec, (communication), Caves on Mt. Greylock/ Iron Pyrite identification, February 2010.

Joe Majchrowski, (communication), Song bird atop Mt. Greylock, May 2010.

Leon "Butch" Parrott, (communication), Speciality Minerals: limestone quarry, Adams, June 2010.

Front Cover: photographer: Kristen Demeo, January 2010

Back Cover: photographer: Cosmo LaViola, January 2009

Tower: photographer: Kristen Demeo, May 2010

Botanical Sketches: Kristen Demeo, 2010

ABOUT THE AUTHOR
Kristen lives in Adams, Massachusetts. A quaint New England town nestled at the base of the highest peak in the state, Mt. Greylock. It is part of the Berkshires; a place where symphonies fill the night air with music. Theatre echoes the voice of playwrights of long ago, and apples hang heavy from the trees in autumn.

We do not inherit Earth

from our ancestors;

we borrow it from our children.

-Native American proverb

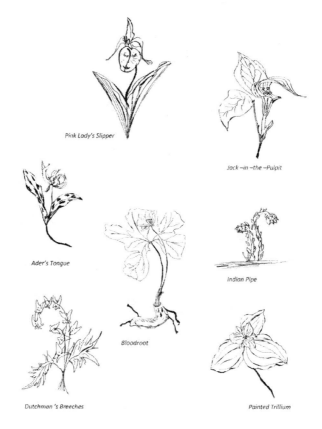

Pink Lady's Slipper

Jack –in –the –Pulpit

Ader's Tongue

Indian Pipe

Bloodroot

Dutchman 's Breeches

Painted Trillium